To Marionne

From Grandma Keesler.
Christmas 1969

WHAT DID I SEE?

MODERN MASTERS BOOKS FOR CHILDREN

PHYLLIS McGINLEY
      The B Book (Illustrated by Robert Jones)

ROBERT GRAVES
      The Big Green Book (Illustrated by Maurice Sendak)

LOUIS UNTERMEYER
      One and One and One (Illustrated by Robert Jones)

JAY WILLIAMS
      Puppy Pie (Illustrated by Wayne Blickenstaff)

WILLIAM JAY SMITH
      What Did I See? (Illustrated by Don Almquist)

JOHN CIARDI
      The Wish Tree (Illustrated by Louis S. Glanzman)

SHIRLEY JACKSON
      Nine Magic Wishes (Illustrated by Lorraine Fox)

PAUL ENGLE
      Who's Afraid? (Illustrated by Ray Prohaska)

EVE MERRIAM
      Funny Town (Illustrated by Evaline Ness)

ARTHUR MILLER
      Jane's Blanket (Illustrated by Al Parker)

WILLIAM JAY SMITH

WHAT DID I SEE?

ILLUSTRATED BY DON ALMQUIST

A MODERN MASTERS BOOK FOR CHILDREN
THE CROWELL-COLLIER PRESS

First Crowell-Collier Press Edition 1962

Library of Congress Catalog Card Number: 62-21356
Copyright ©1962 by William Jay Smith
Illustrations Copyright ©1962 by The Crowell-Collier Publishing Company

I went for a walk,
And what did I see?

I saw a house.

I saw a barn.

I saw a tree.

I went for a walk.
It was warm and sunny.

"Hello," said a bird.
"Hello," said a bunny.

I looked at the house.

I looked at the barn.

I looked at the tree.

Then, all at once, I saw something funny.
All at once everything started to change.

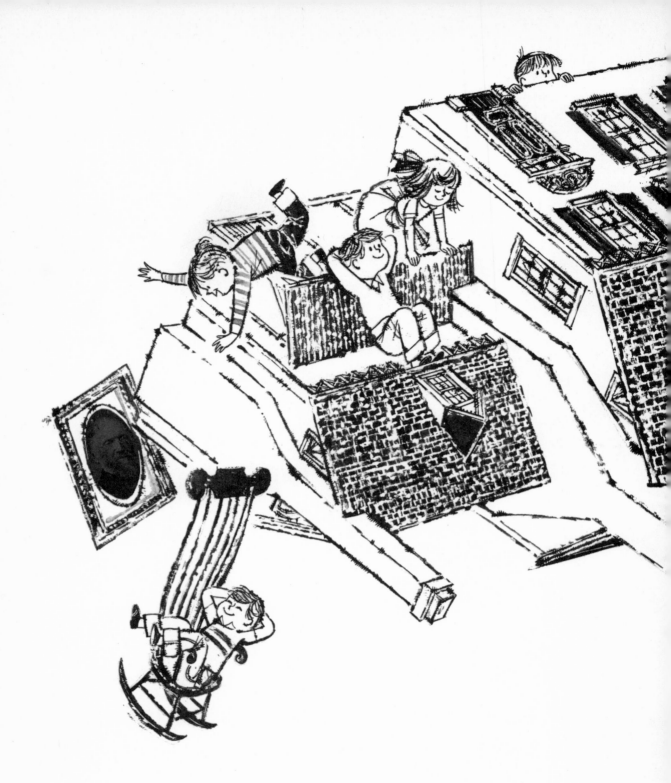

I saw the house with walls and floors,
Chairs and tables, windows and doors,

I saw the house with children inside
All at once fly off the ground,

Fly off like a bird
Round and round
In the big blue sky.

I saw the house go flying by.

I laughed at the children.
They laughed at me.
I laughed at the house as it flew by.

I said to myself, "How can this be?

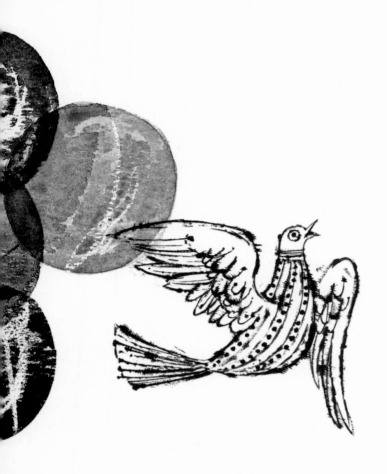

A house is a house.
It's not a balloon.
It can't go flying
Up to the moon!
How can this be?"

I went for a walk,
And what did I see?

I saw the barn
Next to the house
In the tall grass
With all the animals kept inside—
Pigs and chickens, ducks and cows—

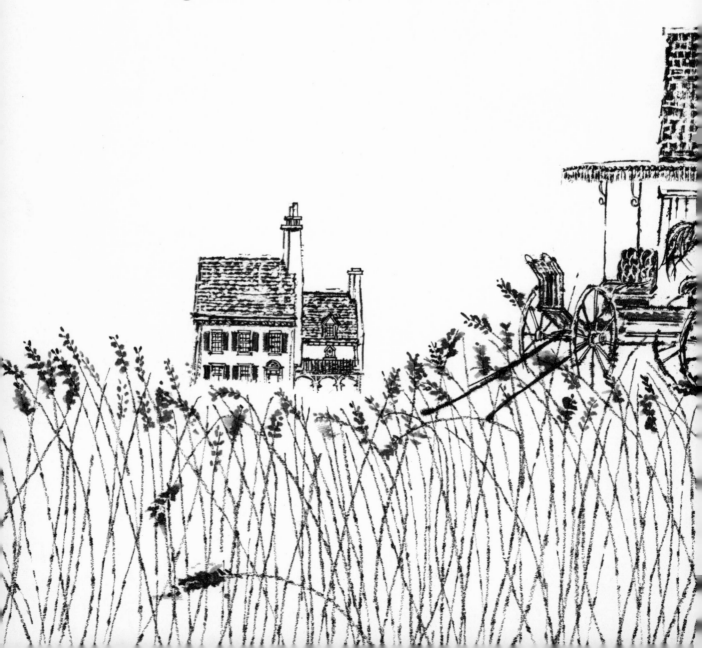

And all at once the water came
Up over the grass and over the ground.
The water came up all around—

And then the barn was a barn no more.
The water came right up to the door.

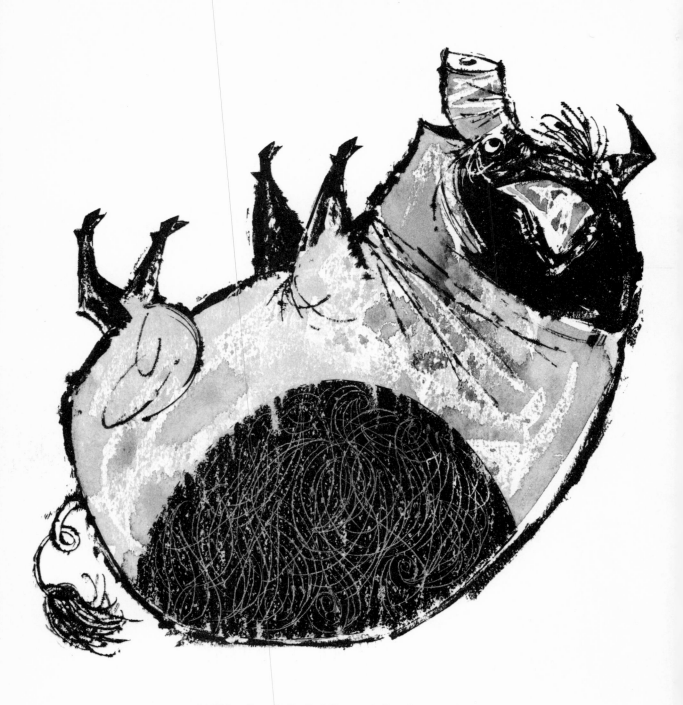

"Oink-Oink!" said the pigs,
"We are sailing away."

"Cluck-Cluck!"

"Moo-Moo!"

"Quack-Quack!"

"Good-by!"

So the animals said as the water came round
And the barn like a boat sailed over the ground.
I laughed as I saw it sailing by
Round and round
In the big blue sky.

I said to myself,
   "How can this be?
   A barn is a barn.
   It's not a boat.
   It cannot sail.
   It cannot float.
   How can this be?"

I went for a walk,
And what did I see?

At the top of a hill
I saw the tree.
It started to dance
On the sunny ground.
It started to dance in the tall green grass.

In its leafy dress of green and gold
I saw it go up over the hill.
With butterflies dancing all around,
Round and round
In the big blue sky,
I laughed as the tree went dancing by.

I said to myself,
　"How can this be?
　　A tree is a tree.
　　It grows in the ground.
　　It can't get up
　　And dance around.
　　How can this be?"

"Not one of these things can really be,"
I said to myself.

"A house can't fly,

A barn can't sail,

A tree can't dance,

No more than a mouse
Can read his mail.
How can this be?"

"How can this be?"
I heard someone say.
"It *could* be, you know,
It could in a way.

In a dream, you know,
Anything can be—
A house can fly,
A barn can sail,
A tree can dance,
A monkey skip rope with his tail.

And even a mouse
Can read his mail.

In a dream, you know,
Things can be funny—

An elephant can hop like a bunny,

A kitten can sit and count his money,

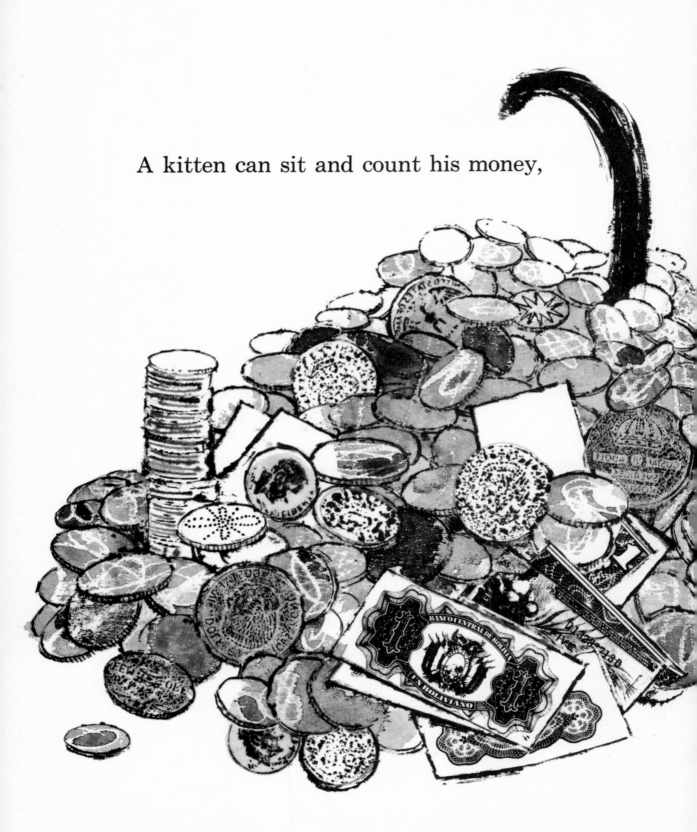

A jack-o-lantern can dry his eyes.

Turkeys and turtles can make mud-pies,

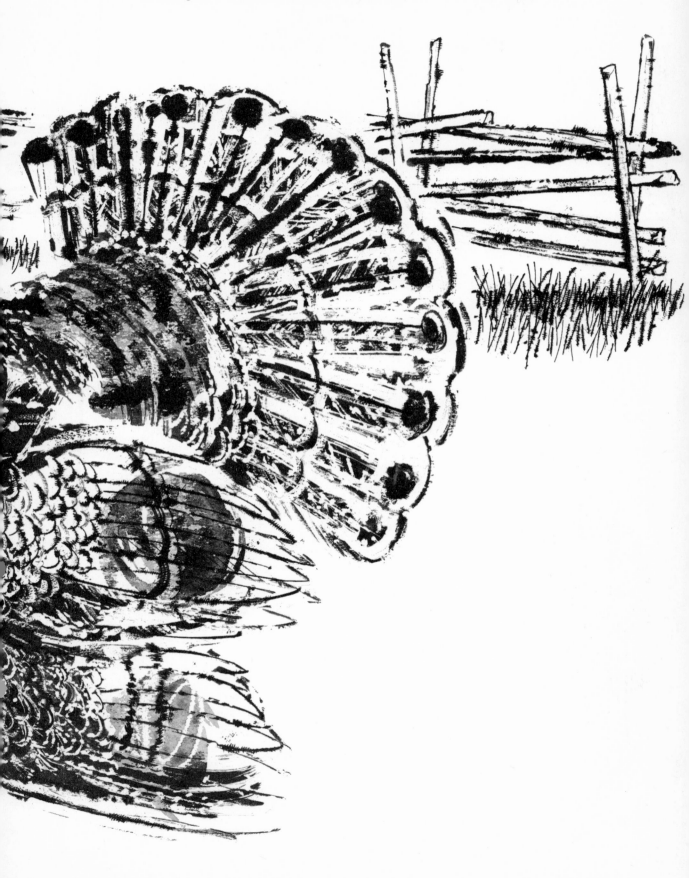

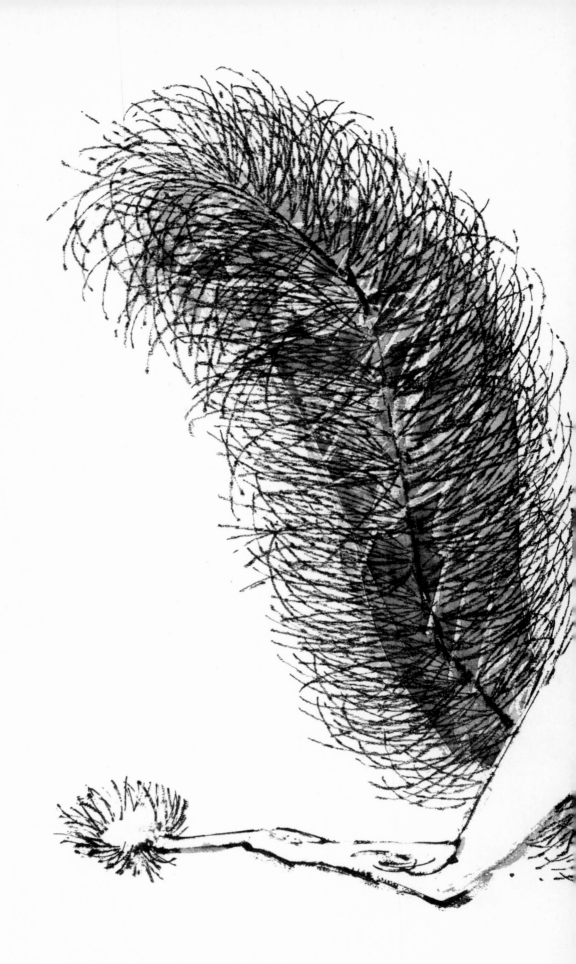

A squirrel can put on a stocking cap.

You have been for a walk,
You have had a nap.
You have been asleep
Here under the tree.

Open your eyes
And look at me!"
I opened my eyes,
And what did I see?

I saw my mother looking at me.

"Let's go for a walk," I said to my mother.

I said to my mother, "Come with me."

So we went for a walk.

It was warm and sunny.
"Hello," said a bird.
"Hello," said a bunny.
We went for a walk,
And what did we see?

We saw a house.

We saw a barn.

We saw a tree.

And we saw how dreams can really be.